Bonnie Marcus Collection

FOOD
JOURNAL

PaRragon

Bath • New York • Singapore • Hong Kong • Cologne • Delhi
Melbourne • Amsterdam • Johannesburg • Shenzhen

When you feel good, it shows...

The Bonnie Marcus Food Journal is more than a logbook for your food and exercise; it's a place to write, read, doodle, and feel inspired—your indispensable guide to the diet dilemmas of a modern girl. We've made sure that it's packed full of little snippets to amuse, advise, or motivate, plus recipes to help to confirm your status as a domestic goddess.

This journey isn't just about losing weight; it's about finding yourself. We want to help you make the most of every day and be mindful about what you put into your body (it is a temple, after all). With a little savvy advice, you can navigate 21st-century womanhood, in heels!

The secret of getting ahead is getting started!

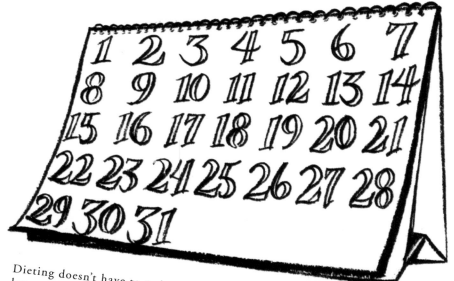

Dieting doesn't have to wait until Monday—don't put it off any longer. Pick a date and stick to it!

What did you eat today?

DATE

	Calories	Fat	Sat Fat	Carbs
Breakfast				
Lunch				
Dinner				
Snacks				
TOTAL				

NOTES

5

Wholewheat Muffins

● **MAKES 10**

1¾ cups wholewheat flour
2 teaspoons baking powder
2 tablespoons light brown sugar
¾ cup finely chopped dried apricots
1 banana, mashed with 1 tablespoon
  orange juice
1 teaspoon finely grated orange rind

1¼ cup skim milk
1 egg, beaten
3 tablespoons canola oil or sunflower oil
2 tablespoons rolled oats
fruit spread, honey, or maple syrup,
  to serve

1. Preheat the oven to 400°F. Place 10 muffin cups in a muffin pan. Sift the flour and baking powder into a mixing bowl, adding any husks that remain in the strainer. Stir in the sugar and chopped apricots.

2. Make a well in the center of the dry ingredients and add the banana, orange rind, milk, beaten egg, and oil. Mix together well to form a thick batter. Divide the batter evenly among the 10 muffin cups.

3. Sprinkle each muffin with a few rolled oats and bake in the preheated oven for 25–30 minutes, or until well-risen and firm to the touch. Transfer the muffins to a wire rack to cool slightly. Serve the muffins warm with a little fruit spread, honey, or maple syrup.

What did you eat today?

DATE

	Calories	Fat	Sat Fat	Carbs
Breakfast				
Lunch				
Dinner				
Snacks				
TOTAL				

NOTES

What did you eat today?

DATE ....

	Calories	Fat	Sat Fat	Carbs

- **Breakfast**
....
....

- **Lunch**
....
....

- **Dinner**
....
....

- **Snacks**
....
....
....
....

TOTAL

- **NOTES**

The people who will love you at your worst...

Add pictures of the ones who love you best!

What did you eat today?

DATE
....

● **Breakfast**
....
....

● **Lunch**
....
....

● **Dinner**
....
....

● **Snacks**
....
....
....

	Calories	Fat	Sat Fat	Carbs
TOTAL				

⚙ NOTES

What did you eat today?

DATE

	Calories	Fat	Sat Fat	Carbs

● **Breakfast**

● **Lunch**

● **Dinner**

● **Snacks**

TOTAL

⚙ **NOTES**

Diet-Friendly Brownie Bites

● **MAKES 36**

6 ounces semisweet chocolate,
   broken into small pieces
2 eggs
1 teaspoon vanilla extract
⅔ cup firmly packed dark brown sugar
⅓ cup sunflower oil, plus extra
   for greasing

4 cooked beets, grated
¾ cup all-purpose flour
¾ teaspoon baking powder
3 tablespoons unsweetened
   cocoa powder

1. Preheat the oven to 350°F. Lightly grease an 8-inch square baking pan and line with parchment paper.

2. Put the chocolate in a heatproof bowl set over a saucepan of gently simmering water and heat until just melted. Remove from the heat.

3. Put the eggs, vanilla, and sugar in a bowl and beat at high speed with an electric mixer for 3–4 minutes, or until pale and creamy. Beat in the oil. Stir in the beet, then sift in the flour, baking powder, and cocoa and fold in. Add the melted chocolate and stir until evenly combined.

4. Spoon the batter into the prepared pan and bake in the preheated oven for 25–30 minutes, or until just firm to the touch. Let cool in the pan, then turn out and let cool completely on a cooling rack. Cut into about 36 bite-size squares and serve.

● **TIP:** Store the cut brownies in an airtight container—they're best eaten within 1–2 days. Uncut and wrapped in plastic wrap, they will keep at room temperature for up to 4 days, or in the freezer up to 3 months. Cut into bite-size squares to serve.

What did you eat today?

	Calories	Fat	Sat Fat	Carbs
DATE				
⬤ **Breakfast**				
⬤ **Lunch**				
⬤ **Dinner**				
⬤ **Snacks**				
TOTAL				

⬤ **NOTES**

It's not shopping,
it's retail therapy!

Be so happy that
when others look
at you, they feel
happy, too!

❀ MAKE A LIST OF ALL THE THINGS THAT MAKE YOU SMILE—EVERY LITTLE TRIUMPH IS WORTH CELEBRATING!

What did you eat today?

DATE ....

	Calories	Fat	Sat Fat	Carbs

● **Breakfast**
....
....

● **Lunch**
....
....

● **Dinner**
....
....

● **Snacks**
....
....
....
....

TOTAL

NOTES

What did you eat today?

	Calories	Fat	Sat Fat	Carbs

DATE

....

● **Breakfast**

....

....

● **Lunch**

....

....

● **Dinner**

....

....

● **Snacks**

....

....

....

....

TOTAL

NOTES

What did you eat today?

DATE

....

🔘 **Breakfast**

....

....

🔘 **Lunch**

....

....

🔘 **Dinner**

....

....

🔘 **Snacks**

....

....

....

....

	Calories	Fat	Sat Fat	Carbs
TOTAL				

🔘 **NOTES**

22

What did you eat today?

DATE

....

- **Breakfast**

....

....

- **Lunch**

....

....

- **Dinner**

....

....

- **Snacks**

....

....

....

....

	Calories	Fat	Sat Fat	Carbs
TOTAL				

- **NOTES**

10 Everyday Superfoods

Your body is a temple, right? Well superfoods are packed with important nutritional elements for optimum mental and physical health. These 10 ingredients are all things that you'll find in the local grocery store, and they won't break the bank, either...

● **APPLES** are your go-to fruit if you're on a diet—an average-size apple contains just 60 calories, and they're low on the glycemic index (GI) so they keep you fuller for longer. Apples are also an excellent source of potassium, which helps to prevent fluid retention and bloating. They say "an apple a day keeps the doctor away" and it's true—regular apple-eaters are proven to have smaller waistlines than those who don't!

● **ORANGES** are a great source of vitamin C, which is a great natural cold remedy—it helps to fight off infections and reduce the length of coughs and sniffles. Choose the fruit instead of a glass of orange juice (which often has added sweeteners) as the average-size orange comes in at just 65 calories.

● **BLUEBERRIES** the original superfood, blueberries are a tasty fruit that can easily be added to everyday eating (bake into muffins, sprinkle over oatmeal, or eat as a snack). Regular consumption of blueberries could help to lower your cholesterol, a key indicator of heart health. And, even better, it's said to be a natural fix for pesky bouts of cystitis.

● **BANANAS** have all the necessary nutrients to make them the ultimate sports snack—complex carbs, potassium, and fiber mean they are a quality fuel for the body, so grab one after a workout to replenish your body. Although quite high in natural sugars, the average-size banana is only around 105 calories—an excellent healthy snack.

● **BROCCOLI** is the stuff of most kids' nightmares, but actually it's a really low-calorie vegetable (only 34 calories per 3½ ounces) that's packed with beneficial nutrients like calcium for healthy bones and teeth. Look out for darker-green broccoli—the darker it is, in fact, the better it is for you!

● **CARROTS** contain carotene, which helps to protect against high cholesterol and its associated heart disease, and it's proven that women who eat at least 5 carrots per week are two-thirds less likely to have a stroke than those who consume none. Be careful, though—a very high intake of carrots can cause carotenemia, which makes the skin appear orange!

● **TOMATOES** are an excellent addition to salads, as they are extremely low in calories (18 calories per 3½ ounces) and just one medium-size tomato contains ¼ of your Recommended Daily Allowance (RDA) of vitamin C. Pick tomatoes that are deep red and ripe, as these contain more lycopene, which helps to prevent blood clots.

● **GARLIC** is renowned for it's strong flavour—and lingering smell—but if you can get past the inevitable garlic-breath, it's a really beneficial addition to your diet. Regular consumption (even in small quantities) can reduce the risk of heart disease.

● **PUMPKIN** contains fat-soluble carotenoids, which help to protect the skin, heart, eyes, brain, and liver (all fatty parts of the body). It also contains malic acid, which is important for cell regeneration. Pumpkin's high water content (which is common to all marrows and squashes) means it is very low in calories: 3½ ounces of peeled, chopped pumpkin is just 13 calories.

● **RED BELL PEPPERS** can contain up to 2 x the amount of vitamin C and 9 x the amount of carotene in green peppers. They are a good source of vitamin A, which is used to repair skin damaged by UV light. An average-size red pepper contains 37 calories, so is a low-calorie ingredient that can be added to all sorts of family-friendly dishes (chili, pasta sauce, savory bakes, and stews).

What did you eat today?

DATE

....

	Calories	Fat	Sat Fat	Carbs

● **Breakfast**

....

....

● **Lunch**

....

....

● **Dinner**

....

....

● **Snacks**

....

....

....

....

TOTAL

● **NOTES**

What did you eat today?

DATE ....

	Calories	Fat	Sat Fat	Carbs
● **Breakfast**				
● **Lunch**				
● **Dinner**				
● **Snacks**				
TOTAL				

● **NOTES**

Mojito Ice Pops

● **MAKES 8**

juice of 6 limes
2½ cups chilled club soda
leaves from 1 bunch of fresh mint
3 limes, cut into wedges
½ cup superfine sugar
2 tablespoons white rum

1. Put the lime juice and club soda into a small bowl and stir together well.

2. Stir in the mint leaves, lime wedges, sugar, and rum. Using a muddler, thick wooden spoon, or mallet, mash together all the ingredients until well blended.

3. Pour the mixture into eight ½-cup ice-pop molds. Divide the lime wedges and mint leaves evenly among them. Insert the ice-pop sticks and freeze for 10–12 hours, or until firm. If you are using store-bought molds with their own plastic sticks, follow the manufacturer's directions for inserting the sticks. If your molds don't come with sticks, use wooden ones. To hold the sticks in place while your ice pop freezes, cover the filled molds with aluminum foil and make a small slit with a sharp knife in the center. Insert the stick and it will be secure until your ice pop is frozen.

4. To unmold the ice pops, dip the frozen molds into warm water for a few seconds and gently release the pops while holding the sticks. Eat within 3 months of freezing.

● **TIP:** Once they're unmolded, ice pops can be eaten right away, but it's best to wait a bit. Wrap pops in plastic food bags or plastic wrap and freeze for at least 30 minutes. This second freezing means the ice pops won't melt as quickly while you're eating them.

No matter how slow you go, you are still lapping everybody on the couch.

Studies have shown that many of us put on weight not because we are eating more than we used to, but because we burn fewer calories through activity. Cars, home appliances, the Internet, TV, office jobs, escalators, and elevators all help to keep us sedentary. Exercise not only helps you to keep your weight stable (and can help you to lose any extra pounds) but also improves sleep patterns, helps lift depression, improves posture, increases strength and mobility, and improves heart and lung health.

The best exercise is anything you can do without huge expense, or adjusting your lifestyle too much. Walking is ideal—you can do it anywhere, any time, and it's free. Try taking the stairs not the elevator, or walking one extra stop instead of taking the bus all the way. Try to do at least 30 minutes a day, five days a week.

You don't have to feel the burn to see the benefit. Burn off some extra calories while cleaning around the house...

Vacuuming—180 Cals*
Dusting—170 Cals*
Gardening—250 Cals*
Mopping floors—190 Cals*
Washing windows—180 Cals*
Ironing—110 Cals*

*Values given are approximate number of calories burned in 1 hour. Calories burned depend on height, weight, and vigor of movement, and will differ from person to person.

What did you eat today?

	Calories	Fat	Sat Fat	Carbs

DATE
....

● **Breakfast**
....
....

● **Lunch**
....
....

● **Dinner**
....
....

● **Snacks**
....
....
....
....

TOTAL

✿ NOTES

❀ TODAY I WISH...

....
....
....
....
....
....
....
....

Turn I wish into I will...

What did you eat today?

DATE

....

	Calories	Fat	Sat Fat	Carbs

● **Breakfast**

....

....

● **Lunch**

....

....

● **Dinner**

....

....

● **Snacks**

....

....

....

....

TOTAL

NOTES

What did you eat today?

DATE
....

	Calories	Fat	Sat Fat	Carbs

🔵 **Breakfast**
....
....

🔵 **Lunch**
....
....

🔵 **Dinner**
....
....

🔵 **Snacks**
....
....
....
....

TOTAL

🔵 **NOTES**

What did you eat today?

DATE ....

	Calories	Fat	Sat Fat	Carbs
Breakfast				
....				
....				
Lunch				
....				
....				
Dinner				
....				
....				
Snacks				
....				
....				
....				
....				
TOTAL				

NOTES

36

What did you eat today?

DATE
....

● **Breakfast**
....
....

● **Lunch**
....
....

● **Dinner**
....
....

● **Snacks**
....
....
....
....

	Calories	Fat	Sat Fat	Carbs
TOTAL				

● **NOTES**

Red Salad with Beets & Radish

● SERVES 4

8 small cooked beets, quartered
1 small red onion, cut into thin wedges
1 bunch radishes, sliced
1 tablespoon chopped fresh mint
½ cup extra virgin olive oil
1 tablespoon whole-grain mustard

1 tablespoon balsamic vinegar
1 tablespoon lemon juice
2 teaspoons honey
salt and pepper
flatbread, to serve

1. Toss together the beet, onion, and radishes and stir in half the mint. Arrange on four serving plates.

2. To make the dressing, put the oil, mustard, vinegar, lemon juice, and honey into a screw-top jar and shake well to mix. Season with salt and pepper to taste.

3. Spoon the dressing over the salad and sprinkle the remaining mint on top. Serve immediately, with flatbread.

Avocado, Feta & Arugula Salad

● **SERVES 4**

2 ripe avocados
4 handfuls arugula
4½ ounces feta cheese, crumbled
½ cup olive oil
2 tablespoons white wine vinegar
1 shallot, finely chopped

1 large ripe tomato, seeded and diced
1 tablespoon lemon juice
1 teaspoon granulated sugar
salt and pepper

1. Halve, peel, pit, and slice the avocados and arrange on a serving dish with the arugula. Top with the feta cheese.

2. To make the dressing, put the oil and vinegar into a saucepan and gently heat, then add the shallot and cook, stirring for 2–3 minutes, until soft. Add the tomatoes, lemon juice, and sugar and gently heat, stirring, for 30 seconds.

3. Season the dressing with salt and pepper, then spoon it over the salad and serve immediately.

What did you eat today?

DATE
....

	Calories	Fat	Sat Fat	Carbs

● **Breakfast**
....
....

● **Lunch**
....
....

● **Dinner**
....
....

● **Snacks**
....
....
....
....

TOTAL

❋ NOTES

What did you eat today?

DATE ....

	Calories	Fat	Sat Fat	Carbs

● **Breakfast**
....
....

● **Lunch**
....
....

● **Dinner**
....
....

● **Snacks**
....
....
....
....

TOTAL

● **NOTES**

What did you eat today?

DATE

. . . .

	Calories	Fat	Sat Fat	Carbs

● **Breakfast**

. . . .

. . . .

● **Lunch**

. . . .

. . . .

● **Dinner**

. . . .

. . . .

● **Snacks**

. . . .

. . . .

. . . .

. . . .

TOTAL

☼ **NOTES**

What did you eat today?

	Calories	Fat	Sat Fat	Carbs

DATE
....

● **Breakfast**
....
....

● **Lunch**
....
....

● **Dinner**
....
....

● **Snacks**
....
....
....
....

TOTAL

● **NOTES**

My favorite
new recipes...

● **RECIPE** ....

Source ....

Ingredients ....

....

....

....

Method ....

....

....

....

....

....

....

....

....

What did you eat today?

DATE

	Calories	Fat	Sat Fat	Carbs
Breakfast				
Lunch				
Dinner				
Snacks				
TOTAL				

NOTES

Never underestimate the restorative powers of a hot bath. Always make time to soak your troubles away.

> Cheers! Here's to a glass of bubbles that comes in at under 100 calories per glass.

Strawberry Fizz

● **SERVES 4**

8 ounces fresh strawberries, hulled
2 tablespoons agave syrup
juice of 1 lime
½ cup crushed ice
½ cup vodka
1¾ cups diet cola
whole strawberries and strips of lime zest, to decorate

1. Put the strawberries, syrup, and lime in a plastic pitcher and process with an electric handheld immersion blender or in a food processor until smooth.

2. Add 2 tablespoons of crushed ice to each of four glasses.

3. Pour the strawberry mixture evenly into each glass, add 2 tablespoons of vodka to each glass, and stir to mix.

4. Fill up the glasses with the cola to taste, place a strawberry and strips of lime zest on the rims, and serve immediately.

● **TIP:** To add an extra-fabulous finish to your low-cal cocktail, make a tray of decorative ice cubes. Half-fill ice-cube trays with water and freeze until firm. Dip edible flowers into cold water, then place in the ice cube trays. Top off with water and freeze.

What did you eat today?

DATE

	Calories	Fat	Sat Fat	Carbs
● **Breakfast**				
● **Lunch**				
● **Dinner**				
● **Snacks**				
TOTAL				

● **NOTES**

What did you eat today?

DATE

	Calories	Fat	Sat Fat	Carbs
Breakfast				
Lunch				
Dinner				
Snacks				
TOTAL				

● NOTES

What did you eat today?

DATE ....

	Calories	Fat	Sat Fat	Carbs

● **Breakfast**
....
....

● **Lunch**
....
....

● **Dinner**
....
....

● **Snacks**
....
....
....

TOTAL

● **NOTES**

What did you eat today?

DATE ....

	Calories	Fat	Sat Fat	Carbs

● **Breakfast**
....
....

● **Lunch**
....
....

● **Dinner**
....
....

● **Snacks**
....
....
....
....

TOTAL

❀ **NOTES**

200-Calorie Chocolate Soufflés

● **MAKES 6**

vegetable oil spray
2 tablespoons unsalted butter
3 ounces semisweet chocolate,
  finely chopped
¾ cup skim milk
¼ cup unsweetened cocoa powder

1 tablespoon all-purpose flour
1 teaspoon vanilla extract
pinch of salt
4 egg whites
½ cup granulated sugar

1. Preheat the oven to 375°F. Spray six ¾-cup ramekins (individual ceramic dishes) with vegetable oil spray. Put the butter, chocolate, and ¼ cup of the milk in a small bowl and microwave on high for 30 seconds. Stir until the chocolate is melted. Add the cocoa powder, flour, vanilla extract, and salt and beat until well mixed. Add the remaining milk and stir to combine.

2. In a large bowl, beat the egg whites with an electric mixer on high speed for about 3 minutes, or until stiff peaks form. Add the sugar, a little at a time, and continue to beat for about another 2 minutes, or until the mixture is thick and glossy.

3. Gently fold a large dollop of the egg mixture into the chocolate mixture and stir to combine using a rubber spatula. Gently fold the chocolate mixture into the remaining egg mixture until well combined.

4. Carefully spoon the mixture into the prepared ramekins and bake in the preheated oven for about 22–25 minutes, or until the soufflés are puffy and dry on the top. Serve immediately.

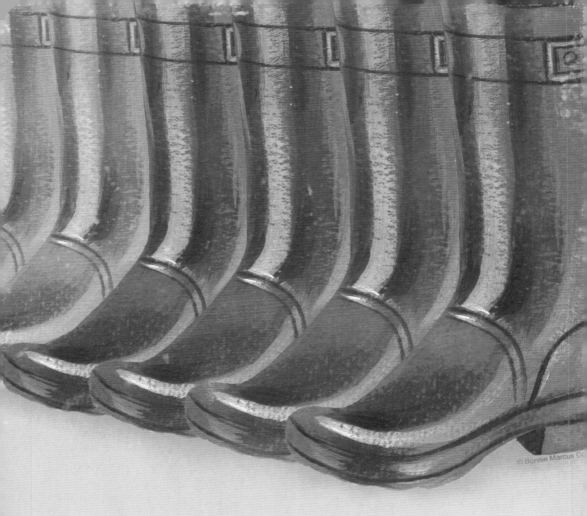

You are never too old to splash in the puddles and dance in the rain!

What did you eat today?

DATE

	Calories	Fat	Sat Fat	Carbs
● **Breakfast**				
● **Lunch**				
● **Dinner**				
● **Snacks**				
TOTAL				

● NOTES

What did you eat today?

	Calories	Fat	Sat Fat	Carbs

DATE

....

● **Breakfast**

....

....

● **Lunch**

....

....

● **Dinner**

....

....

● **Snacks**

....

....

....

....

TOTAL

NOTES

What did you eat today?

DATE

	Calories	Fat	Sat Fat	Carbs

● **Breakfast**

● **Lunch**

● **Dinner**

● **Snacks**

TOTAL

NOTES

What did you eat today?

	Calories	Fat	Sat Fat	Carbs
DATE				
Breakfast				
Lunch				
Dinner				
Snacks				
TOTAL				

NOTES

What did you eat today?

DATE

	Calories	Fat	Sat Fat	Carbs
Breakfast				
Lunch				
Dinner				
Snacks				
TOTAL				

NOTES

A Balanced Diet

A balanced diet means eating a wide variety of foods in the right proportions. If we can balance the major calorie-providing nutrients, such as carbohydrates, fats, and protein, then they should provide all of the other elements essential to a healthy diet—vitamins, minerals, and plant chemical compounds, as well as dietary fiber.

20 PERCENT

5 PERCENT

12 PERCENT

33 PERCENT

30 PERCENT

● 33 PERCENT Fruit and vegetables

These are the richest providers of many vitamins, plant chemicals, and fiber. At least five portions every day are preferable and the ideal balance is two fruits and three vegetables. Choose a rainbow of different colors to be sure you get a complete range of nutrients.

● 30 PERCENT Starchy foods

Starchy foods, such as grains (preferably whole), bread, pasta, and root vegetables provide a range of vitamins, minerals, plant chemicals, and fiber, as well as the calories we need.

● 20 PERCENT Lean meat, eggs, fish, shellfish, nuts, and seeds

Vary your choices within this section; it is good to eat fish regularly (including oily fish), but also have meals that include legumes, such as beans or lentils, or nuts and seeds.

● 12 PERCENT Dairy or soy protein

Including milk, cheese, and yogurt, or calcium-fortified soy milk and yogurts. Cream and cream cheeses aren't included because they contain little protein and a lot of saturated fat.

● 5 PERCENT High fat or high sugar foods

These are what might be called "junk foods" and should be eaten in small amounts (or not at all, if possible). This includes sugar, sugary drinks, cake, cookies, pastries, and confectionery.

Pumpkin & Navy Bean Slimmers' Soup

● **SERVES 4**

1 teaspoon olive oil
1 red onion, chopped
2 garlic cloves, crushed
4 cups peeled, seeded, and chopped
  pumpkin or other winter squash
2 teaspoons smoked paprika
¾ teaspoon crushed red pepper flakes

5–6 fresh sage leaves, finely chopped
3¾ cups vegetable stock
1 (15-ounce) can navy beans, drained
salt and pepper, to taste
crème fraîche and chopped scallions,
  to serve

1. Heat the oil in a large heavy-bottom saucepan and sauté the onion and garlic for 3–4 minutes. Add the pumpkin and cook for an additional 4–5 minutes.

2. Add the paprika, red pepper flakes, and sage and cook for 1 minute, stirring all the time.

3. Add the stock, season with salt and pepper, cover, and simmer for 20–25 minutes, or until the pumpkin is tender. Let the soup cool slightly, then process using an electric handheld immersion blender, until smooth.

4. Stir in the navy beans and heat through for 2–3 minutes. Serve with a spoonful of crème fraîche and a sprinkle of chopped scallions.

● **TIP:** One serving of this super healthy soup is just 130 calories. A portion also contains just 1.5g of fat, of which only 0.5g is saturated fat.

What did you eat today?

DATE

....

● **Breakfast**

....

....

● **Lunch**

....

....

● **Dinner**

....

....

● **Snacks**

....

....

....

	Calories	Fat	Sat Fat	Carbs
TOTAL				

NOTES

Dorothy is proof that with a fabulous pair of heels you can do anything!

Life is sweet!

IT'S OK TO INDULGE ONCE IN A WHILE...

What did you eat today?

DATE ....

	Calories	Fat	Sat Fat	Carbs

● **Breakfast**

● **Lunch**

● **Dinner**

● **Snacks**

TOTAL

● **NOTES**

Peachy Wake-Up Call

● **MAKES 1**

1 medium sweet potato, cut in
  half lengthwise
½-inch piece fresh ginger
3 carrots, scrubbed
3 peaches, halved and pitted
pinch ground mixed spice (optional)

Feed all the ingredients through
the juicer, the sweet potato is quite
hard so make sure that the juicer is
on high speed. Pour the juice into a glass
half-filled with ice and sprinkle with
a little ground mixed spice (if using).

Power-Boosting Beets

● **MAKES 1**

2 raw beets, leaves trimmed off
2 large carrots
2 celery sticks, halved
2-inch piece cucumber
2 red-skinned dessert apples, halved
2 tablespoons ground walnuts

Feed all the vegetables and apples through
the juicer. Stir the finely ground walnuts
into the juice then pour into glasses
half-filled with ice and serve.

70

Spiced Berry Bombshell

● **MAKES 1**

3 large ripe red-skinned plums,
 halved and pitted
handful of red or green curly kale
1 ripe pear, cored and halved
1 cup blackberries
2 tablespoons wheatgerm powder
pinch ground cinnamon

Add the plums and kale to the juicer chute
then add the pear and extract the juice.
Pour the juice into a juicer or blender, add
the blackberries, wheatgerm, a little ground
cinnamon, and a handful of ice. Blitz until
smooth. Add water, if needed. Pour into
a glass and serve.

Strawberry Supercharge

● **MAKES 1**

2 cups strawberries, hulled
½ large pomegranate, seeds popped out
 from the casing
2 apples, halved
crushed ice (optional)

Feed the strawberries, pomegranate
seeds, and apples through the juicer; to
maximize the juice make sure that the
juicer is on low speed. Stir well, then
pour into a glass and drink as soon as
you can on its own or with some crushed
ice (if using).

✿ LIST YOUR LONG-TERM HEALTH GOALS, AND HOW YOU AIM TO GET THERE...

Every masterpiece starts with a blank canvas!

What did you eat today?

	Calories	Fat	Sat Fat	Carbs

DATE ....

● **Breakfast**
....
....

● **Lunch**
....
....

● **Dinner**
....
....

● **Snacks**
....
....
....

TOTAL

☀ NOTES

74

What did you eat today?

DATE

....

● **Breakfast**

....

....

● **Lunch**

....

....

● **Dinner**

....

....

● **Snacks**

....

....

....

....

	Calories	Fat	Sat Fat	Carbs
TOTAL				

● **NOTES**

Girls can do anything boys can do, and we can do it in high heels!

What did you eat today?

DATE

	Calories	Fat	Sat Fat	Carbs

- **Breakfast**

- **Lunch**

- **Dinner**

- **Snacks**

TOTAL

⚙ **NOTES**

Angel Food Cake

● **SERVES 10**

sunflower oil, for greasing
8 extra-large egg whites
1 teaspoon cream of tartar
1 teaspoon almond extract
1¼ cups superfine sugar
1 cup all-purpose flour, plus extra
  for dusting

To decorate
2 cups mixed berries, such as
  raspberries and blueberries
1 tablespoon lemon juice
2 tablespoons confectioners' sugar

1. Preheat the oven to 325°F. Grease and lightly flour a 9-inch tube pan.

2. In a clean, grease-free bowl, beat the egg whites until they hold soft peaks. Add the cream of tartar and beat again until the whites are stiff but not dry. Beat in the almond extract, then add the superfine sugar, a tablespoon at a time, beating hard between each addition. Sift in the flour and fold in lightly and evenly, using a large metal spoon.

3. Spoon the batter into the prepared cake pan. Bake in the preheated oven for 40–45 minutes, or until golden brown. Run the tip of a knife around the edges of the cake to loosen from the pan. Let cool in the pan for 10 minutes, then invert onto a wire rack to cool.

4. To decorate, place the berries, lemon juice, and confectioners' sugar in a saucepan and heat until the sugar has dissolved. Spoon over the top of the cake.

At just 170 calories per serving, this cake is as virtuous as it sounds. Plus, with only 0.5g of fat per slice, you can afford to add a layer of air-light vanilla frosting, if you're feeling naughty!

COFFEE
MORNING
CLASSIC

☼ WRITE DOWN FIVE THINGS THAT MADE YOU HAPPY TODAY...

1. ....
....
....

2. ....
....
....

3. ....
....
....

4. ....
....
....

5. ....
....
....

I have chosen to be happy because it is good for my health!

What did you eat today?

DATE

	Calories	Fat	Sat Fat	Carbs
● **Breakfast**				
● **Lunch**				
● **Dinner**				
● **Snacks**				
TOTAL				

✿ **NOTES**

The most
memorable days
usually end
with the dirtiest
clothes...

What did you eat today?

DATE

	Calories	Fat	Sat Fat	Carbs

● **Breakfast**

● **Lunch**

● **Dinner**

● **Snacks**

TOTAL

● **NOTES**

What did you eat today?

DATE

● **Breakfast**

● **Lunch**

● **Dinner**

● **Snacks**

	Calories	Fat	Sat Fat	Carbs
TOTAL				

● **NOTES**

What did you eat today?

DATE ....

	Calories	Fat	Sat Fat	Carbs
Breakfast				
Lunch				
Dinner				
Snacks				
TOTAL				

● **NOTES**

What did you eat today?

DATE ....

	Calories	Fat	Sat Fat	Carbs

● **Breakfast**

● **Lunch**

● **Dinner**

● **Snacks**

TOTAL

● **NOTES**

What did you eat today?

DATE

	Calories	Fat	Sat Fat	Carbs
Breakfast				
Lunch				
Dinner				
Snacks				
TOTAL				

● **NOTES**

What did you eat today?

DATE

	Calories	Fat	Sat Fat	Carbs

● **Breakfast**

● **Lunch**

● **Dinner**

● **Snacks**

TOTAL

● **NOTES**

What did you eat today?

DATE

	Calories	Fat	Sat Fat	Carbs
Breakfast				
Lunch				
Dinner				
Snacks				
TOTAL				

NOTES

What did you eat today?

	Calories	Fat	Sat Fat	Carbs

● **Breakfast**

● **Lunch**

● **Dinner**

● **Snacks**

TOTAL

● **NOTES**

What did you eat today?

	Calories	Fat	Sat Fat	Carbs
Breakfast				
Lunch				
Dinner				
Snacks				
TOTAL				

NOTES

What did you eat today?

DATE ....

		Calories	Fat	Sat Fat	Carbs

● **Breakfast**
....
....

● **Lunch**
....
....

● **Dinner**
....
....

● **Snacks**
....
....
....
....

TOTAL

✳ **NOTES**

You don't have to
be great to start,
but you have to start
to be great.

Hobbies might seem like a luxury reserved for those who lead a quiet life, but conversely they can be an incredibly important part of a busy lifestyle. A good hobby can provide a slice of work-free time in your schedule, and is a great opportunity to recharge your batteries by doing something you enjoy. It's a great excuse to make a regular fixture with the girls, so use the social aspect of hobbies as another excuse to get motivated. Aerobic activity (no matter how strenuous) encourages regular sleeping patterns, so making time in a full schedule for a workout could actually help you to feel well rested and re-energized.

✿ MAKE A LIST OF NEW HOBBIES YOU COULD ADD TO YOUR WEEKLY SCHEDULE...

....

....

....

....

....

....

....

....

....

....

....

....

....

....

....

....

....

My favorite new recipes...

● **RECIPE** ....

Source ....

Ingredients ....

....

....

....

....

....

Method ....

....

....

....

....

....

....

....

....

....

....

My favorite new recipes...

RECIPE ....

Source ....

Ingredients ....

....

....

....

....

Method ....

....

....

....

....

....

....

....

....

What did you eat today?

DATE

....

	Calories	Fat	Sat Fat	Carbs

● **Breakfast**

....

....

● **Lunch**

....

....

● **Dinner**

....

....

● **Snacks**

....

....

....

TOTAL

☼ NOTES

These mini sweet bites are virtuous because of their size—but at fewer than 150 calories per baby brûlée, you can afford to treat yourself without feeling guilty!

150-Calorie Baby Brûlées

● **MAKES 12**

1 cup blueberries
4 egg yolks
1 teaspoon vanilla extract
½ cup superfine or granulated sugar
1¼ cups heavy cream

1. Preheat the oven to 325°F. Put twelve ¼-cup ovenproof dishes in a large roasting pan and divide the blueberries among them.

2. Put the egg yolks, vanilla, and 3 tablespoons of sugar into a small bowl and mix together, using a fork, until smooth and creamy. Pour the cream into a small, heavy saucepan, bring to a boil, then gradually mix it into the yolks. Pour the mixture through a strainer into the pan before pouring it back into the bowl.

3. Pour the cream mixture over the blueberries. Pour warm water into the roasting pan to come halfway up the sides of the dishes. Bake in the preheated oven for 15 minutes, or until the custard is just set, with a slight wobble in the center.

4. Let cool for 5–10 minutes, then lift the dishes out of the water and transfer to the refrigerator to chill for 3–4 hours.

5. To serve, sprinkle the remaining sugar over the dishes in an even layer, then caramelize it using a cook's blowtorch or under a broiler preheated to hot.

Keep your head
high, and your
heels higher!

What did you eat today?

DATE

....

● **Breakfast**

....

....

● **Lunch**

....

....

● **Dinner**

....

....

● **Snacks**

....

....

....

....

TOTAL

Calories	Fat	Sat Fat	Carbs

NOTES

Light Toffee Popcorn

● **MAKES ABOUT 25 CUPS**

5 tablespoons unsalted butter
½ cup popcorn
¼ cup firmly packed dark brown sugar
2 tablespoons light corn syrup

1. Melt 2 tablespoons of the butter in a large, heavy saucepan. Add the popcorn and swirl the pan to coat the corn evenly.

2. Cover the pan with a tight-fitting lid, reduce the heat to low, and let the corn start popping. Shake the pan a couple of times to move the unpopped pieces to the bottom. As soon as the popping stops, take the pan off the heat and let stand, covered.

3. For the toffee coating, melt the remaining butter in a medium, heavy saucepan. Add the sugar and syrup and cook over high heat, stirring, for 1–2 minutes, or until the sugar has dissolved.

4. Pour the toffee coating over the popped corn, replace the lid on the pan, and shake well. Let cool slightly, then serve immediately.

Skinny Hot Choc

● SERVES 1–2

1 tablespoon granulated sugar
2 tablespoons unsweetened cocoa powder
1 cup skim milk
¼ teaspoon vanilla extract
chocolate curls, to decorate (optional)

1. In a small saucepan, combine the sugar, cocoa powder, and about 2 tablespoons of the milk. Stir to make a paste.

2. Add the remaining milk and heat to a simmer over medium heat. Cook, stirring occasionally, for about 3 minutes, until the cocoa and sugar have completely dissolved.

3. Stir in the vanilla extract and serve immediately, topped with chocolate curls (if using).

Vitamins & Minerals

Some of the most important nutrients for health are those that we need only in small amounts, but are essential for good health. Vitamins and minerals are needed for the day-to-day functioning, protection, and maintenance of our bodies...

● **VITAMINS** that we need regularly but not necessarily every day because they can be stored in the body are:

Vitamin A—For healthy growth, skin, and vision, found mainly in meat, dairy produce, and eggs. The body can also convert carotenoids, found in brightly colored plant foods, into vitamin A.

Vitamin D—For calcium absorption and other functions, found in oily fish and eggs.

Vitamin E—A powerful antioxidant that helps prevent heart disease, found in nuts, seeds, other plant oils, and some other plant foods.

Vitamin K—For normal blood clotting, found in a wide variety of foods.

● **VITAMINS** we need daily, ideally, because they cannot be stored in the body are:

Vitamin C—For the immune system, to help iron absorption, and many other roles, such as an antioxidant. Found in fruit and vegetables.

Vitamin B group—These work together for growth, a healthy nervous system, and food metabolism. Found in meat, fish, legumes, eggs, and dairy produce.

● MINERALS that we often lack enough of are:

Calcium—For healthy bones and with several other roles, found in dairy produce, nuts, seeds, and dried fruit.

Iron—For healthy blood and transportation of oxygen, found in meat, legumes, whole grains, and leafy greens.

Magnesium—For bone density, and a healthy nervous system, heart, and muscles, found in nuts, seeds, and dairy produce.

Potassium—For regulating blood pressure and for a healthy heart, found in meat, fruit, and vegetables.

Zinc—For a healthy immune system, skin, and fertility, found in red meat, shellfish, nuts, and seeds.

Selenium—For a healthy immune system, found in nuts, legumes, and fish.

What did you eat today?

	Calories	Fat	Sat Fat	Carbs

DATE
....

● **Breakfast**
....
....

● **Lunch**
....
....

● **Dinner**
....
....

● **Snacks**
....
....
....
....

TOTAL

● **NOTES**

What did you eat today?

DATE

....

	Calories	Fat	Sat Fat	Carbs

● **Breakfast**

....

....

● **Lunch**

....

....

● **Dinner**

....

....

● **Snacks**

....

....

....

....

TOTAL

● **NOTES**

Veggie Burgers

1 (15-ounce) can red kidney beans,
  drained and rinsed
1 (15-ounce) can chickpeas,
  drained and rinsed
1 egg yolk
1/4 teaspoon smoked paprika
1 cup fresh bread crumbs

3 scallions, finely chopped
vegetable oil, for brushing
4 burger buns, halved
lettuce leaves
tomato slices
4 tablespoons sour cream
salt and pepper, to taste

1. Preheat the barbecue or broiler to high.

2. Put the beans, chickpeas, egg yolk, paprika, bread crumbs, and scallions in a large bowl and gently mix to combine. Season with salt and pepper. Divide the mixture into four and shape into patties. Season the outside of the patties with salt and pepper and lightly brush with oil.

3. Oil the barbecue grate or broiler rack. Cook the burgers for 5 minutes on each side, or until cooked through. Brush the inside of the buns with oil and toast, for 1–2 minutes. Place some lettuce and tomatoes on each bun bottom. Add the burgers and top with sour cream and the bun lids. Serve immediately.

What did you eat today?

DATE

	Calories	Fat	Sat Fat	Carbs

● **Breakfast**

● **Lunch**

● **Dinner**

● **Snacks**

TOTAL

⚙ **NOTES**

Be the type of person
you want to meet!

White Bean & Chicken Chili

● **SERVES 6**

1 tablespoon vegetable oil
1 onion, diced
2 garlic cloves, finely chopped
1 green bell pepper, seeded and diced
1 small jalapeño pepper, seeded and diced
2 teaspoons chili powder
2 teaspoons dried oregano
1 teaspoon ground cumin

1 teaspoon salt
1 (15-ounce) can white beans, such as
  cannellini, rinsed and drained
3 cups gluten-free chicken stock
1 pound cooked chicken breasts, shredded
juice of 1 lime
½ cup chopped cilantro

1. Heat the oil in a large, heavy saucepan over medium-high heat. Add the onion, garlic, bell pepper, and jalapeño and cook, stirring occasionally, for about 5 minutes, or until soft.

2. Add the chili powder, oregano, cumin, and salt and cook, stirring, for about another 30 seconds. Add the beans and stock and bring to a boil. Reduce the heat to medium-low and simmer gently, uncovered, for about 20 minutes.

3. Ladle about half of the bean mixture into a blender or food processor and puree. Return the puree to the pan along with the shredded chicken. Simmer for about 10 minutes, or until heated through. Just before serving, stir in the lime juice and cilantro. Serve immediately.

Chicken & Sun-Dried Tomato Pasta

● **SERVES 6**

3¾ ounces of sun-dried tomatoes
  (not packed in oil)
12 ounces boneless, skinless chicken
  breasts, diced
1 teaspoon salt
½ teaspoon pepper

vegetable oil spray
2 garlic cloves
½ cup fresh basil
1 tablespoon olive oil
10½ ounces dried pasta

1. Put the tomatoes in a small bowl and cover with boiling water. Set aside to soak for about 20 minutes, until soft, then drain, discarding the soaking liquid.

2. Season the chicken with ½ teaspoon of the salt and the pepper. Coat a large, nonstick skillet with the vegetable oil spray and heat over medium-high heat. Add the chicken and cook, stirring occasionally, for about 5 minutes, or until it is cooked through and just beginning to brown. Set aside.

3. Place the rehydrated tomatoes in a food processor along with the garlic and basil and process to a paste. Add the oil and the remaining salt and continue to process until smooth.

4. Cook the pasta according to the package directions. Just before draining, scoop out and set aside about ½ cup of the cooking water. Drain the pasta. Toss the hot pasta with the sun-dried tomato pesto, chicken, and as much of the pasta cooking water as needed to make a sauce to coat the pasta. Serve immediately.

What did you eat today?

DATE ....

	Calories	Fat	Sat Fat	Carbs

● **Breakfast**

....

....

● **Lunch**

....

....

● **Dinner**

....

....

● **Snacks**

....

....

....

....

TOTAL

● **NOTES**

What did you eat today?

	Calories	Fat	Sat Fat	Carbs

● **Breakfast**

● **Lunch**

● **Dinner**

● **Snacks**

TOTAL

● **NOTES**

Youth-Boosting Foods

● WRINKLES

Whatever your age, wrinkles can leave you feeling, well, old! All sorts of lifestyle factors can be linked to wrinkles—smoking, sun damage, squinting, smiling, and frowning—all are responsible for the everlasting impressions.

Vitamin C serums are big news in skin care, and promoted as an excellent preventative measure against wrinkles, but they've got a price tag to match such audacious claims! Science says a diet that's high in vitamin C and linoleic acid means you are less prone to wrinkles. Berries are brilliant, too—packed full of antioxidants that are key to protecting skin cells from damage (and preventing damage and disintegration leads to a longer-lasting youthful look).

Try peaches, strawberries, kiwi, and blueberries—they won't turn back time, but they can help to slow the ticking clock!

● DRY SKIN

As your body ages, it produces less oil from the sebaceous glands—this can mean skin that's dry, itchy, and prone to eruption (no fun at all). Suddenly all that teenage greasiness doesn't seem so bad.

The best thing you can do to keep your skin looking radiant is drink water—and plenty of it! Creams and serums might provide short-term relief, but good hydration is essential for a good foundation (and it's cheaper!) It's universally accepted that 64 ounces of water per day is how much your body needs—but temper this according to your own body, if it feels good then keep at it! Beyond just water, omega-3 fatty acids are the go-to nutrient that will help soften dry skin and plump it out.

Try fish for a high omega-3 content (salmon and tuna are ideal) or flaxseed, avocado, and walnuts are also good. Vitamin A is good for dried-out, flaky skin, too—and is easily found in dark, leafy greens like spinach and broccoli.

● SUN DAMAGE

Sun damage has a nasty habit of creeping up on you—and prevention is key to ensuring your skin looks tip-top in years to come. Leathery skin, wrinkles, and brown spots are all increasingly harder to reverse the older you get, and beyond the superficial, overexposure can have serious consequences.

Obviously food should never be used to replace a good sunscreen when it comes to limiting sun exposure, but adding a few tomatoes into your daily diet can't hurt. A recent study indicated that lycopene-rich foods, like tomatoes, can improve the skin's ability to protect against UV rays. Adding green tea to your daily routine is also a good defense against the dangers of the sun: the natural anti-inflammatory constituents have been shown to protect against melanoma.

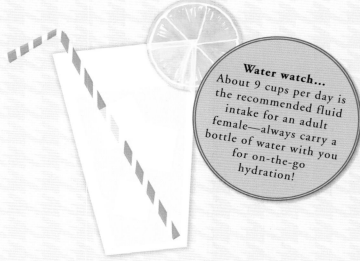

Water watch...
About 9 cups per day is the recommended fluid intake for an adult female—always carry a bottle of water with you for on-the-go hydration!

Chocolate Brownie Mix

● **MAKES 6 (1-PINT JARS)**

6 cups all-purpose flour
1½ teaspoons salt
3 cups light brown sugar
6 cups granulated sugar

4 cups unsweetened cocoa powder
3 cups (about 1 pound) toasted, chopped
  hazelnuts (or other nuts)
3 cups mini semisweet chocolate chips

To prepare the gift jars, add 1 cup of the flour to each of 6 pint-sized canning jars. Next, add ¼ teaspoon of salt and ½ cup of brown sugar. Next add 1 cup of granulated sugar, then ⅔ cup of cocoa powder, ½ cup of chopped nuts, and ½ cup of chocolate chips. The brownie mix will keep for up to 6 months. Store tightly covered in a cool, dry place.

Attach a tag to each jar with these instructions:
1. Preheat the oven to 350°F and oil a 9 x 13-inch pan.

2. Transfer the brownie mix from the jar to a large mixing bowl. In a small mixing bowl, beat together 2 large eggs, 2 tablespoons milk, and 1 teaspoon vanilla extract. Add the egg mixture to the dry ingredients and mix until well combined. Stir in ½ cup of melted butter and mix to combine.

3. Transfer the batter to the prepared pan and bake in the preheated oven for about 20 minutes, until the top is dry and a toothpick inserted into the center comes out mostly clean. Cool completely in the pan on a cooling rack. Serve at room temperature.

Blueberry Pancake Mix

● **MAKES 6 (1-PINT JARS)**

6 cups all-purpose flour
2 tablespoons baking powder
1 tablespoon baking soda
¾ cup granulated sugar
1 tablespoon ground cinnamon

¾ cup brown sugar
1½ cups dried blueberries
¾ cup chopped pecans

To prepare the gift jars, add 1 cup of flour to each of 6 pint-sized canning jars. Top with 1 teaspoon of baking powder, ½ teaspoon of baking soda, 2 tablespoons of granulated sugar, ½ teaspoon of cinnamon, 2 tablespoons of brown sugar, ¼ cup of blueberries, and 2 tablespoons of pecans. Top each jar with a lid and close it tightly. The pancake mix will keep for up to 6 months. Store tightly covered in a cool, dry place.

Attach a tag to each jar with these instructions:
1. Whisk 1 cup of buttermilk or milk and 1 egg together in a large bowl. Add the mix from the jar and 1 tablespoon of melted butter and mix to combine well.

2. Melt a little butter in a skillet set over medium-high heat. Ladle the batter into the hot pan, about ¼ cup at a time. Cook for 2–3 minutes, until bubbles form on the top of the batter, burst, and are not immediately filled in by more batter. Flip the pancake over and cook for another 2 minutes or so, until the second side is golden brown. Continue until all of the batter has been used up. Serve hot, drizzled with maple syrup.

Traditional Lemonade

● **SERVES 4**

3 ripe lemons
½ cup plus 1 tablespoon granulated sugar, or to taste
3½ cups boiling water
cracked ice cubes
lemon slices, to decorate

1. Thinly pare the lemon rind.

2. Put the lemon rind into a heatproof bowl with the sugar. Add the boiling water and stir until the sugar has dissolved. Cover and let cool.

3. Squeeze the juice from the lemons and pour into the cooled syrup. Strain into a jug. Taste and add more sugar, if needed.

4. Fill 4 highball glasses with cracked ice, pour in the lemonade, and dress with the lemon slices.

"When life gives you lemons, make lemonade!"

Turn can't
into can
and dreams
into plans!

☀ WRITE DOWN FIVE THINGS THAT YOU WANT TO ACHIEVE IN THE FUTURE…

1. ....

2. ....

3. ....

4. ....

5. ....

What did you eat today?

DATE

	Calories	Fat	Sat Fat	Carbs

● **Breakfast**

● **Lunch**

● **Dinner**

● **Snacks**

TOTAL

☼ **NOTES**

What did you eat today?

DATE ....

	Calories	Fat	Sat Fat	Carbs

● **Breakfast**
....
....

● **Lunch**
....
....

● **Dinner**
....
....

● **Snacks**
....
....
....
....

TOTAL

● **NOTES**

Exfoliating Body Scrub

Mix 1 tablespoon of sea salt, 2 tablespoons of olive oil, 1 tablespoon of thick honey, and 2–3 drops of rose, sweet fennel, or juniper oil together in a bowl to make a runny paste. Rub gently onto skin with a circular motion and rinse off with warm water.

Exfoliating Face Scrub

Mix 1 tablespoon of honey with 2 tablespoons finely ground almonds and ½ teaspoon lemon juice. Rub gently onto face and rinse off with warm water.

Antioxidant Face Masks

DRY SKIN

Take 1 tablespoon of rolled oats and rub well between your fingers. Steep in a cup of boiling water for 20 minutes. Strain, then mix the oats with 1 tablespoon honey, 1 egg yolk, and 1 tablespoon plain yogurt. Apply to the skin with cotton balls and leave on for 15 minutes.

SENSITIVE SKIN

Mix 1 teaspoon aloe vera gel with 1 tablespoon plain yogurt. Apply and leave for 15 minutes.

OILY SKIN

Mix 1 tablespoon dry fuller's earth (available from some make-up supply companies) with 1 egg yolk, ¼ mashed avocado, and a little witch hazel to create a smooth mixture, Apply to the skin and leave on for 15 minutes.

MATURE SKIN

Mash a ripe avocado with a little olive oil and apply to the skin. Leave on for 15 minutes.

PAMPER TIME

* Use treatments on the day of making. Avoid contact with eyes. If treatments get into the eyes, rinse well with warm water.

What did you eat today?

DATE

	Calories	Fat	Sat Fat	Carbs
Breakfast				
Lunch				
Dinner				
Snacks				
TOTAL				

NOTES

What did you eat today?

DATE

....

	Calories	Fat	Sat Fat	Carbs

● **Breakfast**

....

....

● **Lunch**

....

....

● **Dinner**

....

....

● **Snacks**

....

....

....

TOTAL | | | |

❀ NOTES

Don't Eat That, Do Eat This!

● **BREAKFAST**

Swap that... Blueberry muffin and whole milk latte to go. A small takeout coffee with a sugar-filled muffin can add up to over 500 calories (that's ¼ of the recommended daily 2,000 calorie intake for a woman).

For this... Oatmeal topped with sliced banana and chopped pecans. The oats are rich in soluble fiber, which is a low-GI food and releases sugars slowly to keep you fuller for longer. Adding banana (or berries, if you like!) is an easy way to chalk up one of your recommended five-a-day fruits and vegetables. Nuts contain healthy fats which have been shown to help improve brain function and increase concentration if incorporated into your diet on a daily basis.

● **LUNCH**

Swap that... Classic club sandwich on white bread, with turkey, bacon, and mayo. White bread has almost no nutritional value, and many find that it makes them feel bloated (so not a good afternoon look). Plus, mayonnaise is packed with fats, as is bacon.

For this... Chunky vegetable soup with a wholewheat roll, followed by a yogurt and a piece of fresh fruit (see, when you pick the right foods, you can actually enjoy more!) Soup is any dieter's go-to-lunch and it's light and filling, and wholewheat bread provides fiber (for healthy digestion). You can even afford to add a pat of butter to the roll, since you're being so good! Yogurt provides calcium, which is essential for healthy bones, teeth, hair, and nails—it's true: you are what you eat! Fresh fruit is a sweet treat that counts as another of those all important five-a-day.

● **DINNER**

Swap that... Chinese takeout. We've all been there, dialing for takeout at the end of a long day... but an average serving of sweet and sour chicken with fried rice and shrimp toast can contain in excess of 1,500 calories. With that in mind, it's a no-brainer to make your own, more virtuous version.

For this... Chicken and vegetable stir-fry with brown rice. Chicken is a great all-rounder: filled with flavor, super-lean, and high in protein—it's a must for dieters. Adding your favorite vegetables to any meal is a low-calorie way to increase volume and nutritional value. Brown rice should replace white rice in your pantry. Not only will it keep you fuller for longer, but it's packed with important B vitamins, too.

Did you know?
A ½-cup measure of fruit juice counts as one of your five-a-day—but it has to be unsweetened juice.

Did you know?
Whole grain foods (like wholegrain bread, brown rice, and wholewheat pasta) release sugars slowly, keeping you fuller for longer. Aim for 3–6 servings per day.

Did you know?
Peppermint tea is nature's stomach soother—it is a fantastic sickness remedy, ideal if you feel bloated or queasy after eating too much!

What did you eat today?

	Calories	Fat	Sat Fat	Carbs

DATE
....

● **Breakfast**
....
....

● **Lunch**
....
....

● **Dinner**
....
....

● **Snacks**
....
....
....

TOTAL [ ] [ ] [ ] [ ]

❋ NOTES

What did you eat today?

	Calories	Fat	Sat Fat	Carbs

DATE
....

● **Breakfast**
....
....

● **Lunch**
....
....

● **Dinner**
....
....

● **Snacks**
....
....
....
....

TOTAL

NOTES

What did you eat today?

DATE

....

 Breakfast

....

....

 Lunch

....

....

 Dinner

....

....

 Snacks

....

....

....

....

	Calories	Fat	Sat Fat	Carbs
TOTAL				

NOTES

What did you eat today?

	Calories	Fat	Sat Fat	Carbs
DATE				
⬤ **Breakfast**				
⬤ **Lunch**				
⬤ **Dinner**				
⬤ **Snacks**				
TOTAL				

 NOTES

What did you eat today?

	Calories	Fat	Sat Fat	Carbs

DATE
....

● **Breakfast**
....
....

● **Lunch**
....
....

● **Dinner**
....
....

● **Snacks**
....
....
....

TOTAL ☐ ☐ ☐ ☐

✿ NOTES

What did you eat today?

DATE

	Calories	Fat	Sat Fat	Carbs

- **Breakfast**

- **Lunch**

- **Dinner**

- **Snacks**

TOTAL

☼ **NOTES**

CHOCOLATE
CHEAT

Low-Cal Coffee Ice Cream

● **SERVES 6**

2 ounces semisweet chocolate
1 cup ricotta cheese
⅓ cup low-fat plain yogurt
⅓ cup granulated sugar
¾ cup strong black coffee,
  cooled and chilled

½ teaspoon ground cinnamon
dash of vanilla extract

1. Grate the chocolate and set aside. Put the ricotta cheese, yogurt, and sugar in a blender or food processor and process until a smooth puree forms. Transfer to a large bowl and beat in the coffee, cinnamon, vanilla extract, and half of the grated chocolate.

2. Spoon the mixture into a freezerproof container and freeze for 1½ hours, or until slushy. Remove from the freezer, turn into a bowl, and beat. Return to the container and freeze for 1½ hours.

3. Repeat this beating and freezing process two times before serving in scoops, decorated with the remaining grated chocolate. Alternatively, leave in the freezer until 15 minutes before serving, then transfer to the refrigerator to soften slightly before scooping.

● **TIP:** Homemade ice cream tends to harden over time if stored in the freezer for too long, but this ice cream will keep well for up to three months in a tightly sealed container.

Destiny is all about the
choices we make and
the chances we take!

This edition published by Parragon Books Ltd in 2013 and distributed by

Parragon Inc.
440 Park Avenue South, 13th Floor
New York, NY 10016
www.parragon.com

Project managed by Alice Blackledge
Internal design by Amy Child

ISBN 978-1-4723-2981-3

Printed in China

NOTES FOR THE READER

This book uses standard kitchen measuring spoons and cups. All spoon and cup measurements are level unless otherwise indicated. Unless otherwise stated, milk is assumed to be whole, eggs are large, individual vegetables are medium, and pepper is freshly ground black pepper. Unless otherwise stated, all root vegetables should be peeled prior to using.

Garnishes, decorations, and serving suggestions are all optional and not necessarily included in the recipe ingredients or method. Any optional ingredients and seasoning to taste are not included in the nutritional analysis. The times given are only an approximate guide. Preparation times differ according to the techniques used by different people and the cooking times may also vary from those given. Optional ingredients, variations, or serving suggestions have not been included in the time calculations.

Consult your doctor before following any new diet or fitness plans.

PICTURE ACKNOWLEDGMENTS
Page 62–63: Five food groups © Maximilian Stock Ltd/Getty Images